A PURPLE
Poetry
PAINTBOX

Chosen by John Foster

Oxford University Press

Oxford University Press, Walton St, Oxford OX2 6DP

Oxford   New York
Athens   Auckland   Bangkok   Bombay
Calcutta   Cape Town   Dar es Salaam   Delhi
Florence   Hong Kong   Istanbul   Karachi
Kuala Lumpur   Madras   Madrid   Melbourne
Mexico City   Nairobi   Paris   Singapore
Taipei   Tokyo   Toronto

and associated companies in
Berlin   Ibadan

© Oxford University Press 1996

Oxford is a trade mark of Oxford University Press

First published in paperback 1996
First published in hardback 1996

A CIP catalogue record for this book is available
from the British Library

Illustrations by

Rowan Barnes-Murphy, John Bendall-Brunello, Margaret Chamberlain, Ben Cort,
John Dyke, Jane Gedye, Charlotte Hard, David Johnson, Jan Lewis, Angela
Denise Lindsay, Frances Lloyd, Alan Marks, David Mostyn, Graham Round, Chris Smedley,
Lesley Smith, Lisa Smith, Karen Stevenson, Martin Ursell, Sarah Warburton

ISBN 0 19 916993 4 (paperback)
ISBN 0 19 916994 2 (hardback)

Printed in Hong Kong

Contents

Things which go bump

There's a ghost in our cupboard,
A monster behind the door.
A large green dragon peering
Through a crack in the floor.

A pair of giant bats
Flapping round my bed.
A fierce dinosaur,
Its eyes flashing red.

A creature standing still
In the shadows of the night.
So where do they all go
When I turn on the light?

Andrew Collett

5

A strange morning

Strange things happened
when I woke today.
My shoes got up
and walked away.

And when I tried
to butter my bread
it turned
and buttered me instead.

A voice from the teapot
began to speak:
'Don't pour me yet,
I'm much too weak!'

The cat keeps sitting
on my head.
I think I'll just
go back to bed!

Irene Rawnsley

7

Tricks

For my first trick
I will pull a silver dollar
from this little girl's collar.

'Oh no you can't!'
'Oh yes I can!'

For my second trick
I will turn this little boy
into a tiny, talking toy.

'Oh no you can't!'
'Oh yes I can!'

For my third trick
I will pull a black bat
from this gentleman's hat.

'Oh no you can't!'
'Oh yes I can!'

And for my final trick
I will need a final cheer.
I will climb into this box
and disappear!

'Oh no you can't!'
'Oh yes I —

Pie Corbett

The flight

Something happened
yesterday,
our class teacher
blew away!

We saw her standing
by her chair
and, suddenly,
she wasn't there!

Something whisked her
into the sky.
We saw her flapping,
floating by.

We watched her drifting
like a kite
till she disappeared
from sight.

Something happened
yesterday,
our class teacher
blew away.

Jean Kenward

The lake monster

In the deep, dark forest
Is a deep, dark lake,
In the deep, dark water
Lurks a long, dark snake.

Or is it a dragon?
Or some kind of whale?
No one knows exactly
but it's got a long tail.

Moving through the water
It twists in loops and humps.
It's got a strange-shaped head
With bulging eyes and bumps.

It doesn't surface often,
Which is really just as well,
For some think it's unlucky —
Strange are the tales they tell.

And those who see it tremble,
Those who see it quake,
The long, dark creature
In the deep, dark lake.

Daphne Lister

The watching crocodile

The crafty crocodile
always keeps
one eye open
when the other eye sleeps.

He lies in the river
pretending to doze,
and waits for a fish
to swim past his nose.

Snap! go his jaws;
the meal is gone.
He smiles and waits
for another one.

Take care, little fishes
as you swim by.
Remember, remember
the crocodile's eye.

Irene Rawnsley

17

The garden pond

There's something in the garden pond:
A monster, huge and dark,
As slimy as a conger eel,
As hungry as a shark.

There's something in the garden pond:
I've seen it roll and squirm,
All muddy, long and slippery
Like one enormous worm.

There's something in the garden pond:
It's eaten all the fish,
If you go down the garden path
You'll see it splash and splish,

You'll hear its nasty slithering,
Its bubble and its fizz,
There's something in the garden pond,
There is! There is! There is!

Richard James

The giant tortoise

It stretched out its neck
And it started to crawl.
It crawled through a fence
And it crawled through a wall.

When the giant tortoise moves
Nothing can stop it.

It crawled past the lions
And the kangaroo.
It crawled through a gate
And escaped from the zoo.

When the giant tortoise moves
Nothing can stop it.

It crawled up the road.
It crawled into town.
It knocked three lamps
And a pillar box down.

When the giant tortoise moves
Nothing can stop it.

It flattened a policeman.
It flattened a tree.
What will it flatten next?
Don't ask me!

When the giant tortoise moves
Nothing can stop it.

Richard James

23

I'd like to be an astronaut

I'd like to be an astronaut
Zooming through the stars.
I'd visit lots of planets
Like Jupiter and Mars.

I'd like to roam the spaceways
Where no one's ever been,
Where planets orbit double suns
And where the skies are green.

I'd walk in alien jungles
On beaches wild and free,
And where the only footprints
Are those made by me.

I'd see the strangest deserts,
And maybe in the sands
I'd find a ruined city
Raised by alien hands.

I'd find a thousand treasures,
And then perhaps one day,
I'd meet a fellow traveller
In the Milky Way.

An alien from a planet
In a distant galaxy,
Roaming through the spaceways —
Just like me.

Tony Bradman

The cave

Can you be daring?
Can you be brave?
Will you come down
to explore the cave?

We'll put on our boots
and carefully tramp
down through the darkness,
all slimy and damp.

They say there's a chest
a hundred years old.
It's spilling over
with jewels and gold.

The pirates left it
and never returned.
Their ship caught fire
and the map got burned.

So I'll take the torch
and you take the sack.
Let's go down there
and bring some back.

But hush! There's a dragon
who just might waken,
if he hears any of it
being taken.

Tony Mitton

In our attic

I went up in our attic,
Climbing every creaking stair,
And looked for hidden treasure
That I knew was waiting there.

But then I started screaming.
It echoed through the house.
Instead of finding golden coins
I found a little mouse.

Clive Webster

Our dragon

Do you like our dragon?
Tissue-paper scales,
Eyes are yoghurt cartons,
Sea-shells for his nails.
Teeth are made from pasta,
Red net – fiery breath,
Tape-recorded roaring,
Scares you all to death!

Wendy Larmont

Buried treasure

I went into the garden.
I dug down in the ground
To look for buried treasure
And this is what I found:

Crawly things
Creepy things
Things with shiny tails
Centipedes
Millepedes
Snails snails snails
Creepy things
Crawly things
Little beady bugs
Millepedes
Centipedes
Slugs slugs slugs.

Richard James

Grandad's wonderful marrow

It was huge, it was striped,
it was yellow and green,
the biggest, the fattest
that ever was seen.
It was watered and polished,
that vegetable marrow,
too big for the garden,
too big for the barrow
and Grandad said proudly,
'I'm boasting I know,
but we can't fail to win
at the vegetable show.'

Poor Grandad, that evening
the rain wouldn't stop
and his beautiful marrow
swelled up and went – POP!

Marian Swinger

I wonder

I watch my grandad plant his seeds
And then I watch them grow,
And how they spring up into flowers
I'll never never know.

I wonder if I took 10p
And put it in the ground
Would it grow like Grandad's seeds
Into a million pounds?

Clive Webster

Ghosts in the town

In this town
The Romans walked,
They built these walls,
They joked and talked.

And there's a place,
Some people say,
Roman soldiers
Still walk today.

Daphne Lister

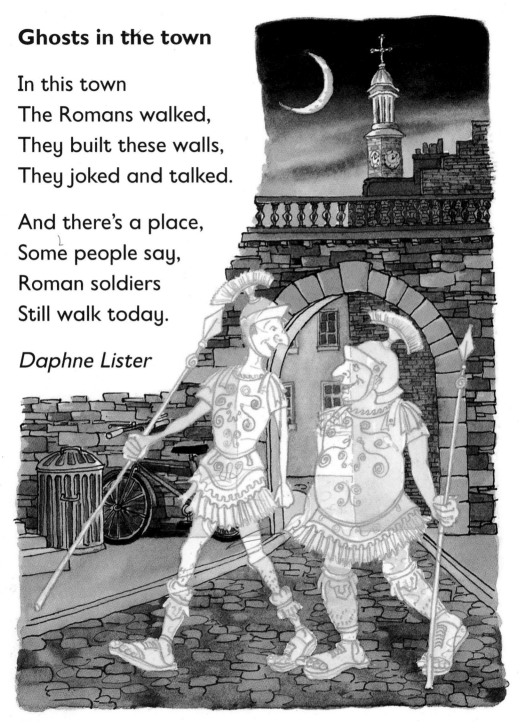

Busy feet

Along the busy pavement
lots of busy feet.
Stand and look and listen
then cross the busy street.
Popping in the busy shop
to buy some food to eat.
Hopping on the busy bus
and wobbling to a seat.
Along the busy pavement,
Along the busy street
hopping, shopping never stopping
busy, busy feet.

Mandy Coe

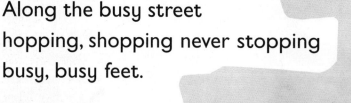

39

Bounce-a-ball at playtime

We're all friends at playtime
and we all play bounce-a-ball.
It's bounce-a-ball to Emma
and it's bounce-a-ball to Paul.
It's bounce-a-ball to Ahmed
and it's bounce-a-ball to Faz.
It's bounce-a-ball to Peter
and it's bounce-a-ball to Jazz.
It's bounce-a-ball to Tracey
and it's bounce-a-ball to Sam.
It's bounce-a-ball to Rachel
and it's bounce-a-ball to Pam.
We play at bounce-a-ball
until our playtime ends.
I play at bounce-a-ball
with all my best best friends.

Wes Magee

Sam's staying with us

Sam is one of my friends.
Today he's very sad.
His mum's gone into hospital
and Sam's got no dad.

My mum's invited Sam
to stay at our big house.
He looks upset and tearful
and he's quiet as a mouse.

We'll have fried egg and chips
and then we'll watch TV.
While Sam's mum is in hospital
Sam is staying with me.

Wes Magee

The dares

They dared me to climb a tree.
I did!
And grazed my knee.

They dared me to jump on the bed.
I did!
And bumped my head.

They dared me to paint teacher red.
I didn't!
I dared them instead.

Brenda Williams

First and last

When a friendship's broken
And it just won't mend,
I've still got
One special friend.
To her I know
I can always come;
She's my first and last
Best friend:
She's Mum.

Eric Finney

Band practice

Terry toots a trumpet.
Dinah bangs a drum.
Gary twangs a steel guitar.
Poor old Mum!

David Orme

Music

Music is invisible,
invisible as air.
You cannot see it,
cannot touch it,
but you know it's there.

It enters through your ears
and it starts to swirl around.
It seems to fill your body
with its rhythm and its sound.

Music is like magic.
It puts you in a trance.
It sets your body moving
and makes your feelings dance.

Music is a mystery.
It seems to cast a spell.
When music really gets to work
then everything feels well.

Tony Mitton

When I close my eyes

When I close my eyes at night,
Lying in my bed,
My pillow fills with stories.
Legends fill my head.

Stories of mighty kings
And giants running tall,
Legends of fierce monsters
And fairies very small.

Stories from China,
Where dragons never die,
And legends from India
Where elephants can fly.

When I close my eyes at night,
Lying in my bed,
My pillow fills with stories.
Legends fill my head.

Andrew Collett

The cat and the rat

A cat and a rat
once went to sea
in a boat they made
from the trunk of a tree.

But the sun was hot
and the sea was deep.
The rat grew hungry.
The cat fell asleep.

Rat nibbled a meal
from the side of the boat.
It tasted good.
They were still afloat,

So he nibbled and nibbled
a little bit more.
Soon the boat was sinking.
Rat swam to the shore.

The wet cat in a fury
followed him fast.
Rat hid in a hole
till the danger was past.

And since that time
where the story ends,
cats and rats
have never been friends.

Irene Rawnsley

Anansi and the moon

Spiderman Anansi
went walking in the night.
Suddenly he noticed
a shining silver light.

He went to have a closer look,
and what was it he found?
A great big shiny silver pearl
lying on the ground.

'Ah!', cried Anansi.
'What a lovely sight!
I'll take it home to give my boys,
and fill them with delight.'

But when Anansi showed it,
the boys could not agree.
They all began to argue, saying,
'Give it just to me!'

So, in the end, Anansi
threw it far and high.
It settled there among the stars,
floating in the sky.

And if you look at night-time
you'll see it hanging there:
a lovely round and silver moon
for all of us to share.

Tony Mitton

The time machine

Roll up, roll up, and on you climb,
I'll take you travelling back through time.
I'll show you things you've never seen.
All aboard my time machine!

Count down from ten. We're off so fast
That years and years are whizzing past.
We've stopped. Where are we? In a wood.
A man in green: it's Robin Hood!

And off again through history,
Let's stop in forty-five BC.
Look! Romans marching to and fro.
They don't look friendly. Time to go.

And further back and further back
We land now on a forest track.
No human footprints on the ground.
No people yet, so what's that sound?

A crash, a grunt, a groan, a roar —
Look out! A long lost dinosaur!
Quick, back on board, count down from ten —
Phew! Just in time, we're home again.

Richard James

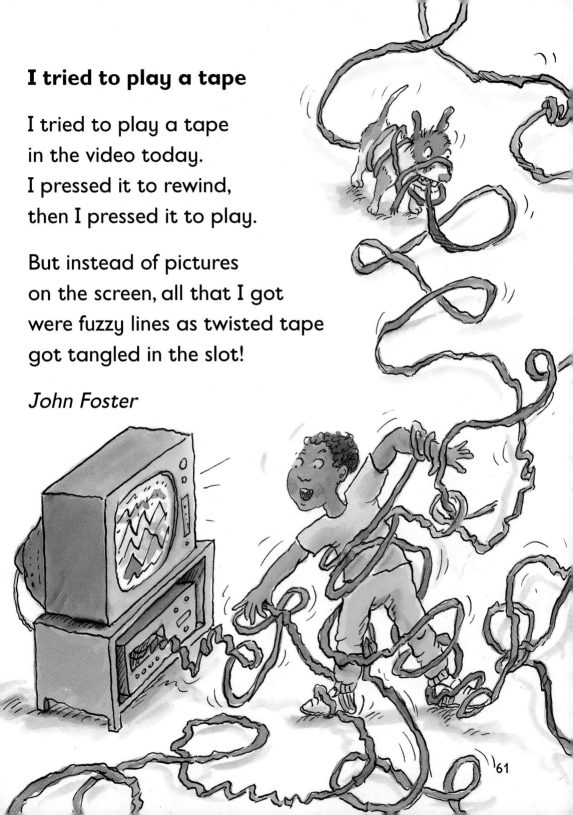

I tried to play a tape

I tried to play a tape
in the video today.
I pressed it to rewind,
then I pressed it to play.

But instead of pictures
on the screen, all that I got
were fuzzy lines as twisted tape
got tangled in the slot!

John Foster

The computer

Samantha Bean,
Samantha Bean,
Sat far too close
To the computer screen.

While she was playing
'Sonic Death Ride',
A hand leapt out
And dragged her inside.

John Coldwell

Index of first lines

Acknowledgements

The Editor and Publisher are grateful for permission to include the following poems:

Tony Bradman for 'I'd like to be an astronaut' © 1996 Tony Bradman; Mandy Coe for 'Busy feet' © 1996 Mandy Coe; John Coldwell for 'The computer' © 1996 John Coldwell; Andrew Collett for 'Things which go bump' and 'When I close my eyes' both © 1996 Andrew Collett; Pie Corbett for 'Tricks' © 1996 Pie Corbett; Eric Finney for 'First and last' © 1996 Eric Finney; John Foster for 'I tried to play a tape' © 1996 John Foster; Richard James for 'Buried Treasure', 'The garden pond', 'The giant tortoise' and 'The time machine' all © 1996 Richard James; Jean Kenward for 'The flight' © 1996 Jean Kenward; Wendy Larmont for 'Our dragon' © 1996 Wendy Larmont; Daphne Lister for 'Ghosts in the town' and 'The lake monster' both © 1996 Daphne Lister; Wes Magee for 'Bounce-a-ball at playtime' and 'Sam's staying with us' both © 1996 Wes Magee; Tony Mitton for 'Anansi and the moon', 'Music' and 'The cave' all © 1996 Tony Mitton; David Orme for 'Band practice' © 1996 David Orme; Irene Rawnsley for 'A strange morning', 'The cat and the rat' and 'The watching crocodile' all © 1996 Irene Rawnsley; Marian Swinger for 'Grandad's wonderful marrow' © 1996 Marian Swinger; Clive Webster for 'In our attic' and 'I wonder' both © 1996 Clive Webster; Brenda Williams for 'The dares' © 1996 Brenda Williams.

Every effort has been made to contact the owners of copyright material, but if any omissions have been made, owners may contact the Publisher, and correct acknowledgement will be made in future editions.